Barnaby goes by Bus

Liz Lewis

Geographical Association

Hurry up Barnaby, find the stop.
Here comes the bus with the open top.

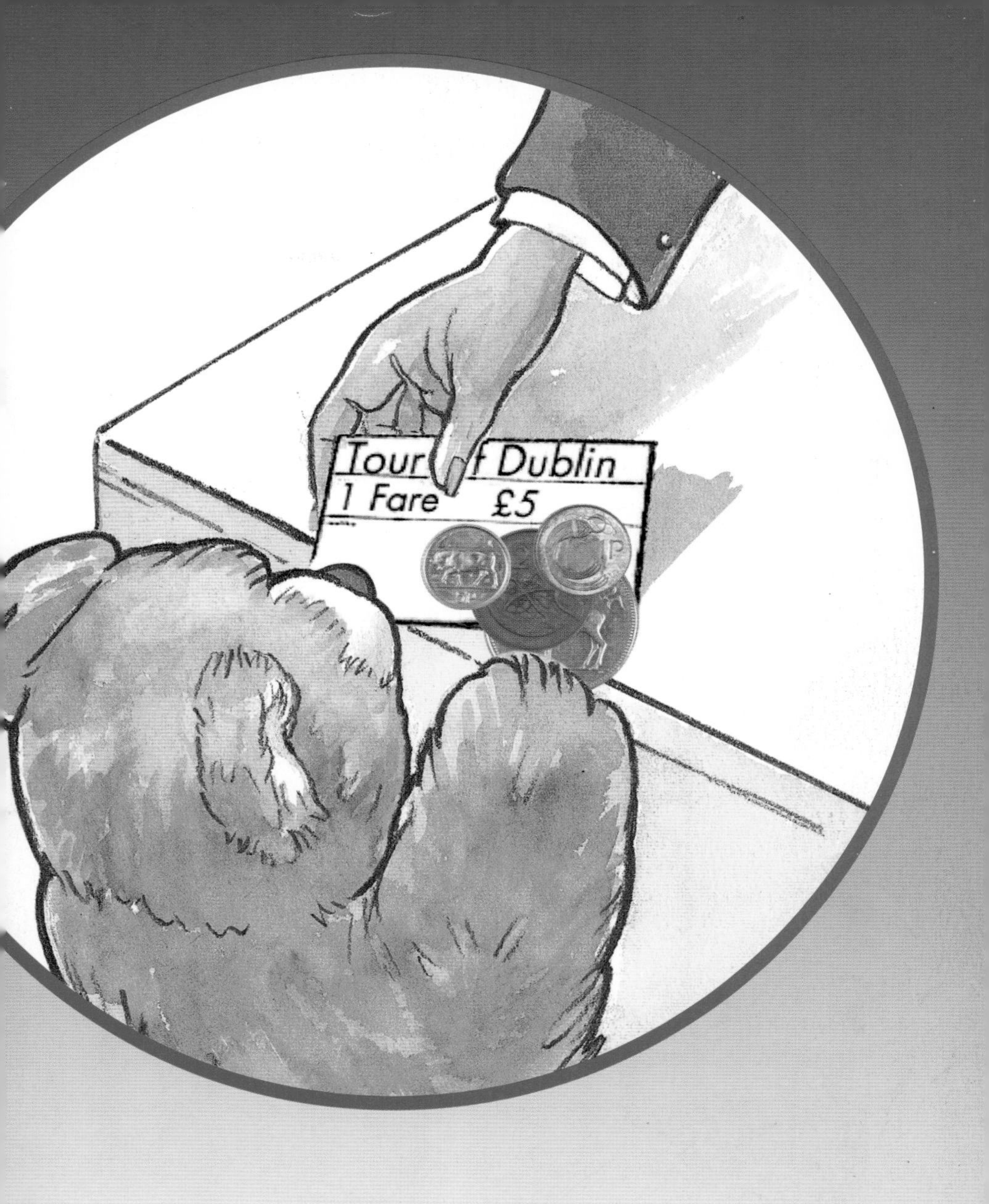

Hop on Barnaby, pay your fare.
Climb upstairs, there are seats up there.

Look out Barnaby, what can you spy?
Buildings so tall
they hide the
sky.

Look around Barnaby, what's over there?
Trees and flowers in a pretty square.

Photo: Conor Sheehan

Look at that Barnaby, what does it say?
Dublin Castle,
open today.

Photo: Irish Tourist Board

Sniff the air Barnaby, can you smell beer?
GUINNESS
Photo: Guiness/Fennel Photography
Yes, my Dad would like it here.
STOP

Look down Barnaby, the lights are green. But the bus has stopped. What can it mean?

Listen Barnaby, was that a bark? People are walking their dogs in that park.

Look left, Barnaby, here is the zoo.
With lions and tigers and bears like you.

We are back by the river, it's on our right.
Lots more bridges have come into sight.

Photo: Keewi Photography

'Goodbye,' says the guide, 'that's all for today.' 'Enjoy the rest of your holiday.'

'Thank you,' says Barnaby, a smile on his face. 'I do like Dublin, it's a beautiful place!'